Learn
How to Draw

_____

This Activity Book Belongs To:

www.engagebooks.com

Design © 2021 Engage Books (Activities)
Design by: Lauren Dick

ISBN 978-1-77476-270-7 (softcover)

✏️ Get creative as you complete the image!

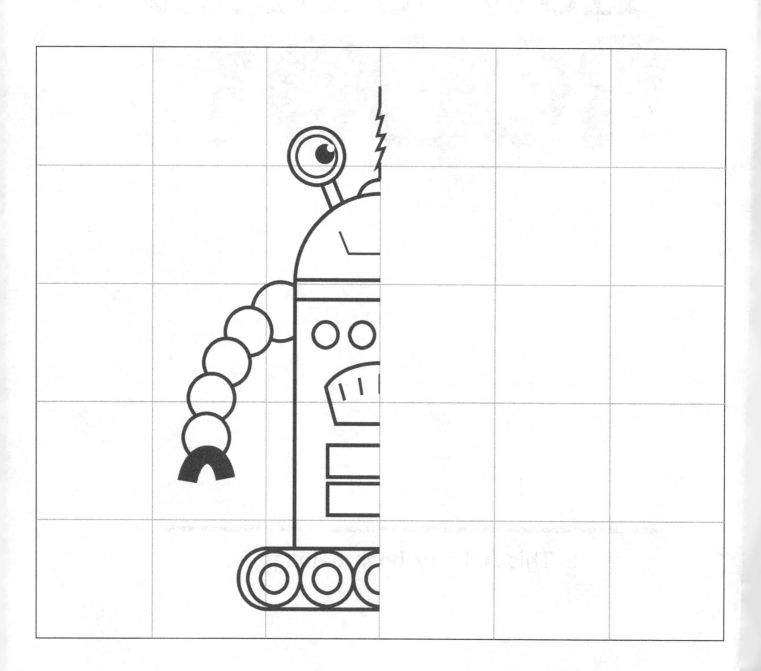

Get creative as you complete the image!

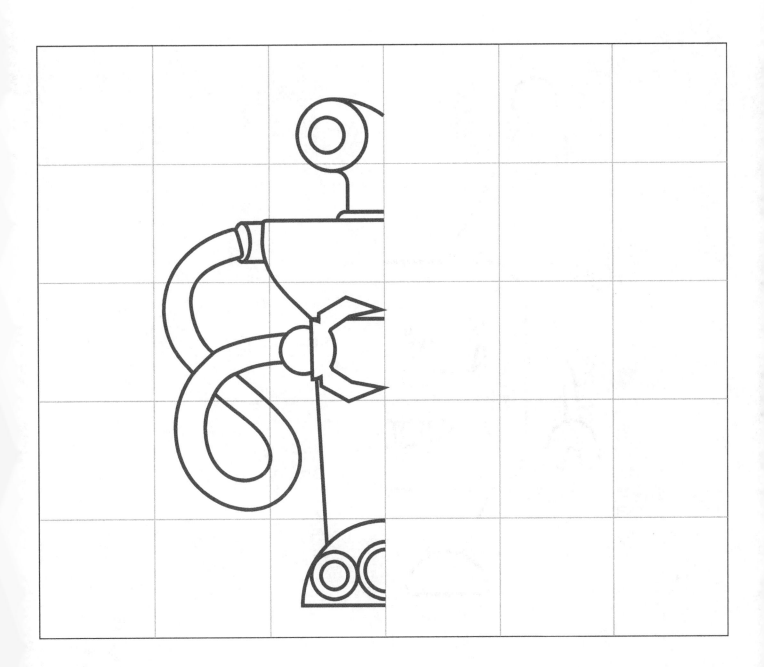

 Get creative as you complete the image!

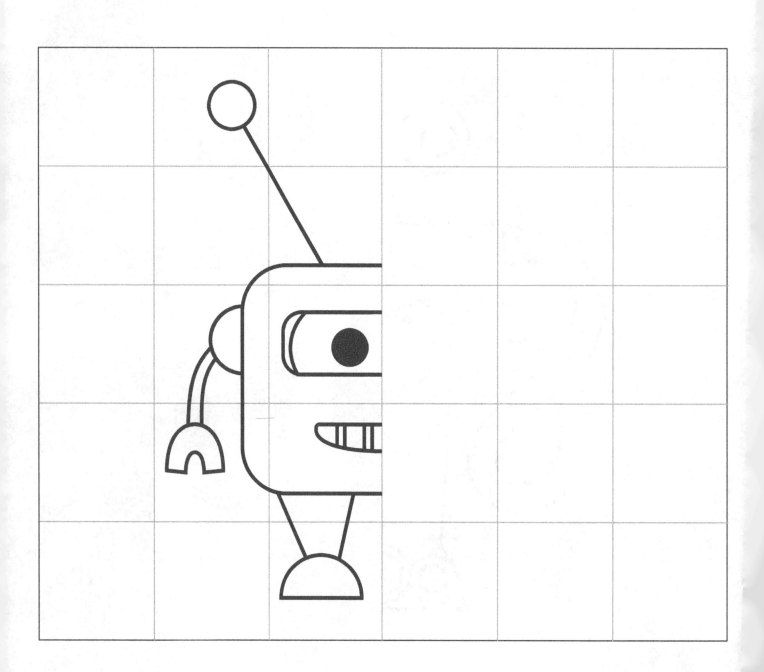

Get creative as you complete the image!

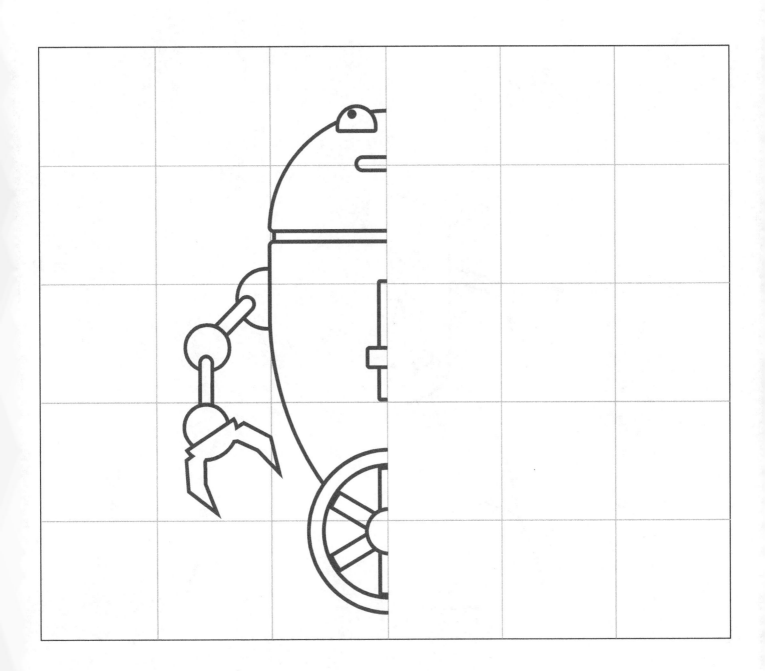

Get creative as you complete the image!

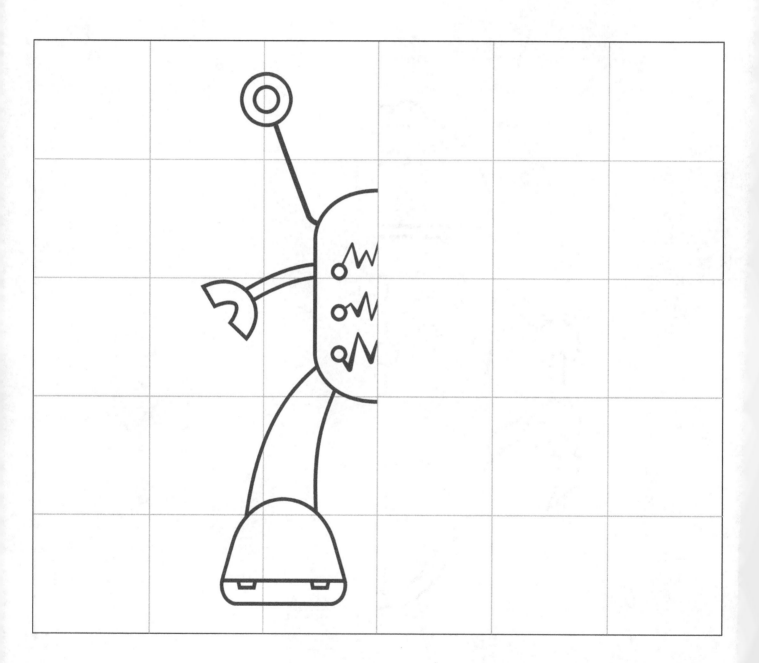

Get creative as you complete the image!

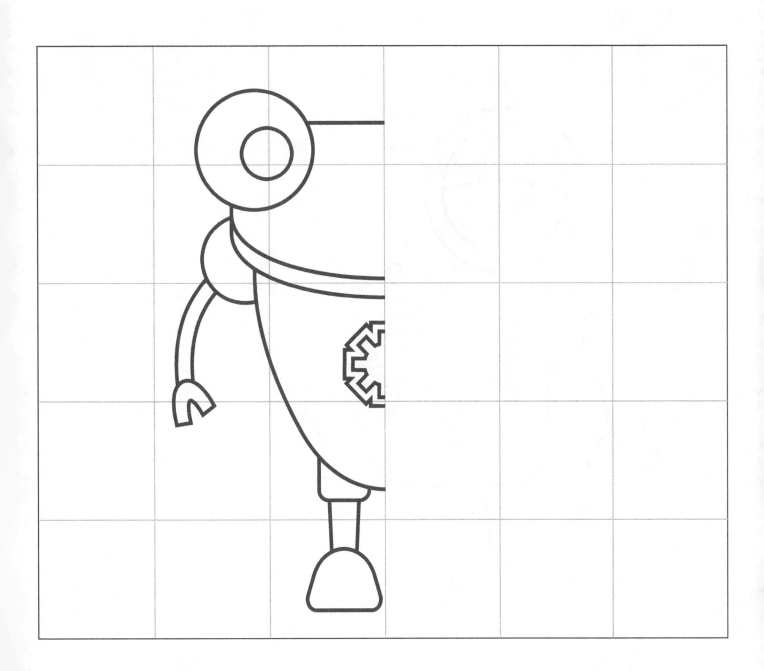

Get creative as you complete the image!

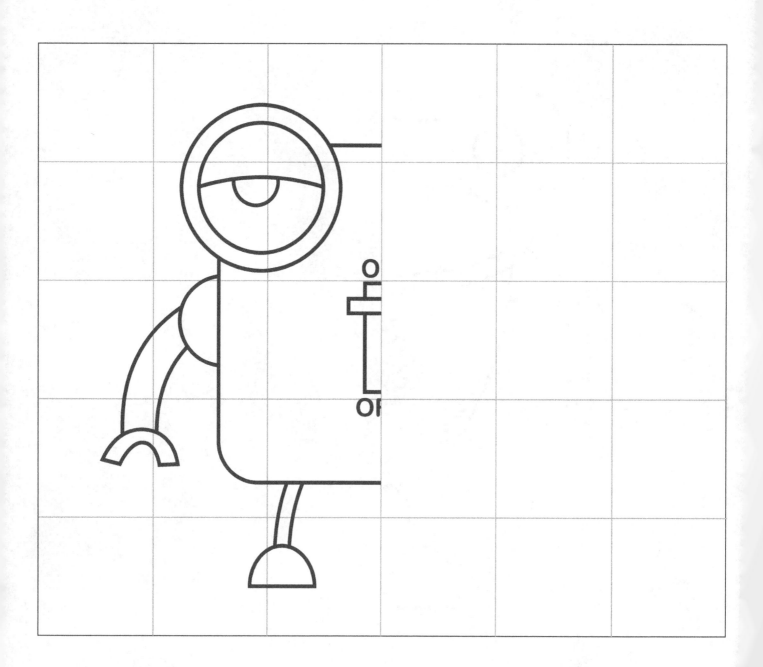

Get creative as you complete the image!

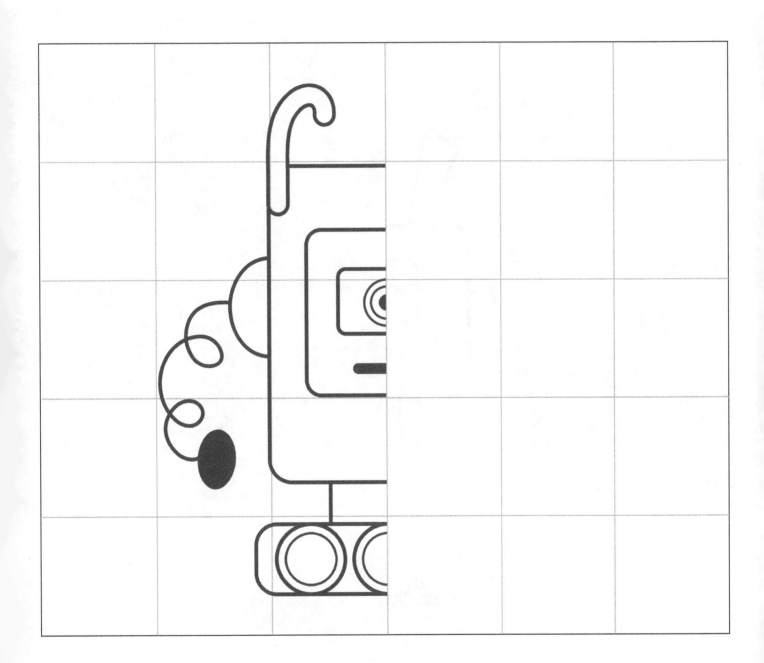

 Get creative as you complete the image!

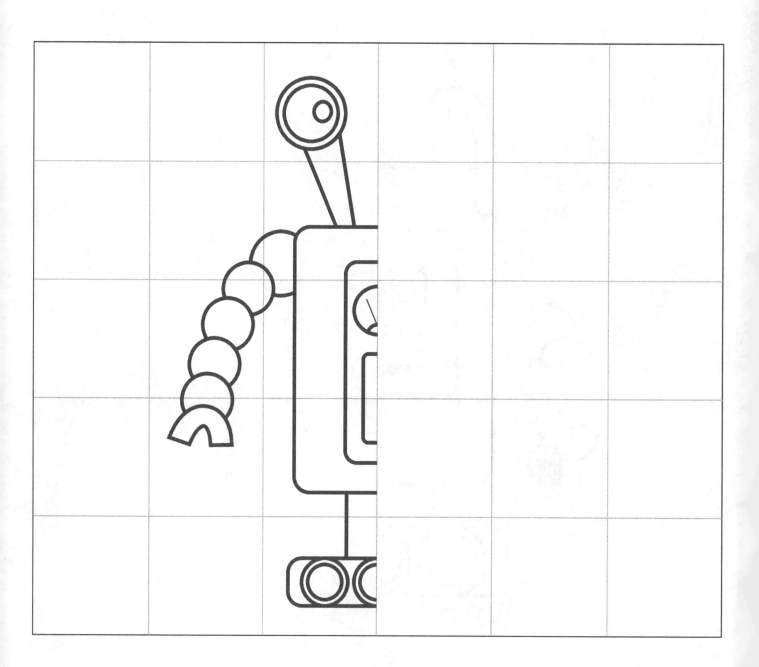

Get creative as you complete the image!

Get creative as you complete the image!

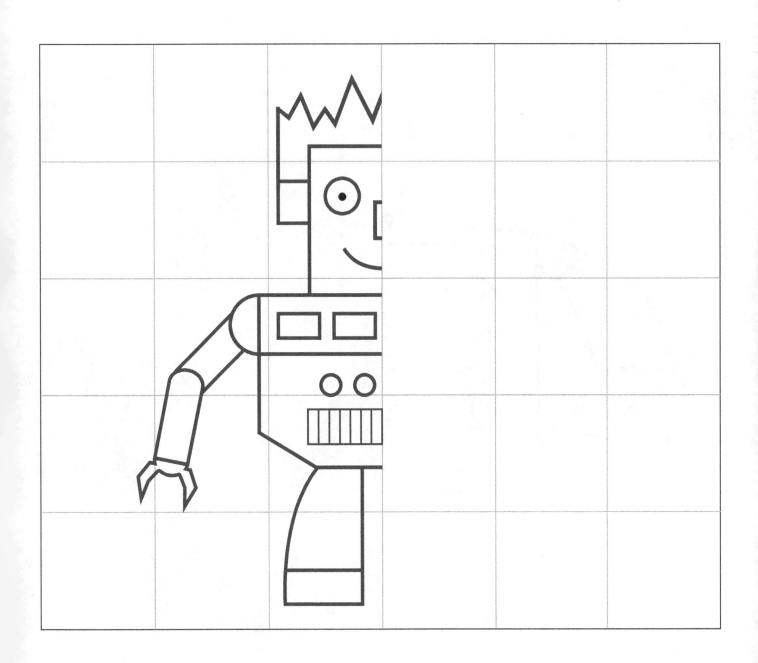

✏️ Get creative as you complete the image!

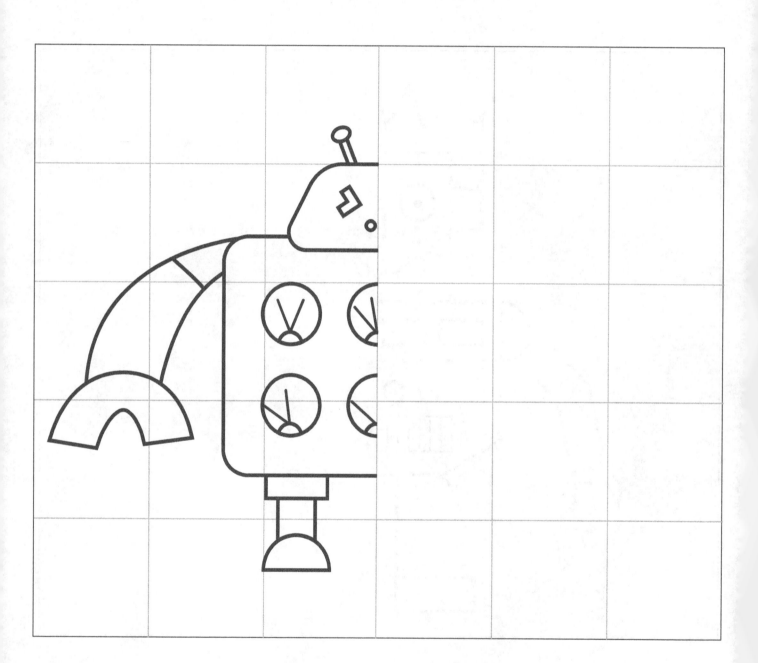

Get creative as you complete the image!

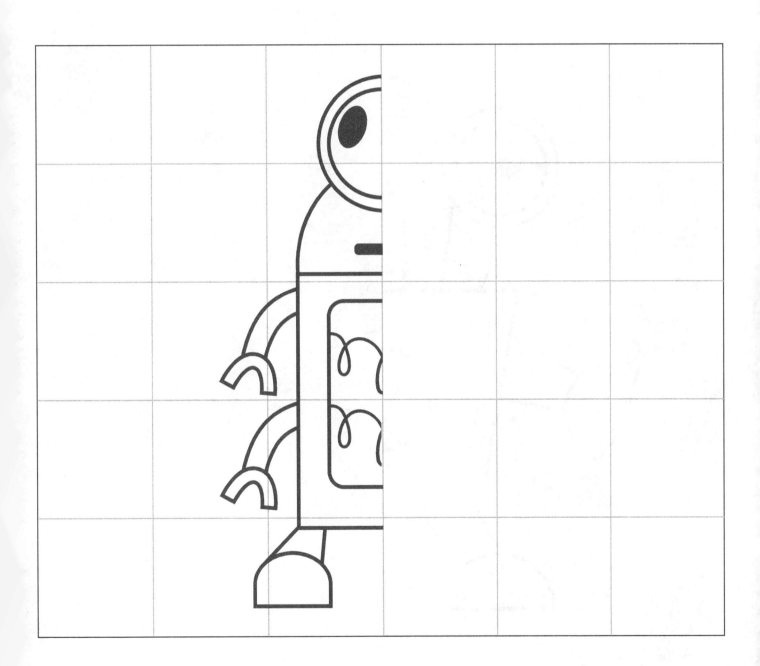

 Get creative as you complete the image!

Get creative as you complete the image!

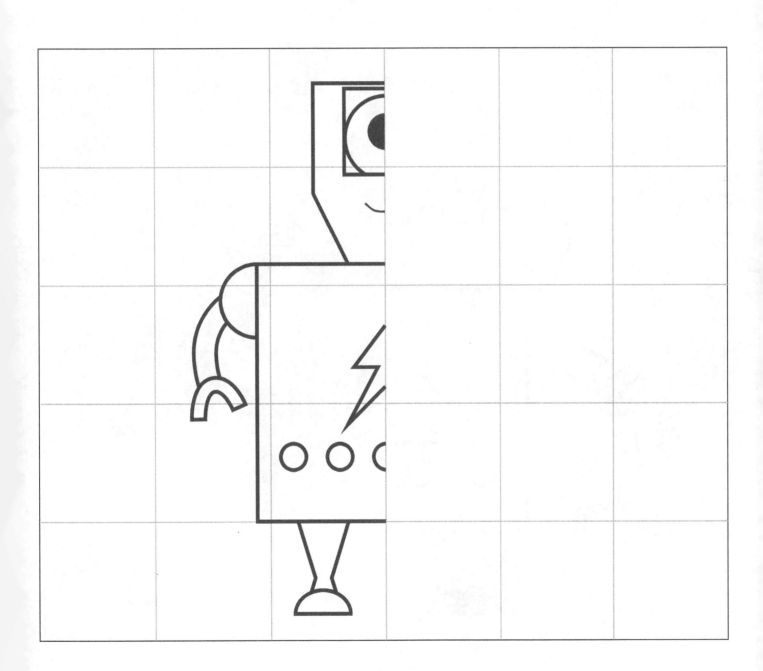

 Get creative as you complete the image!

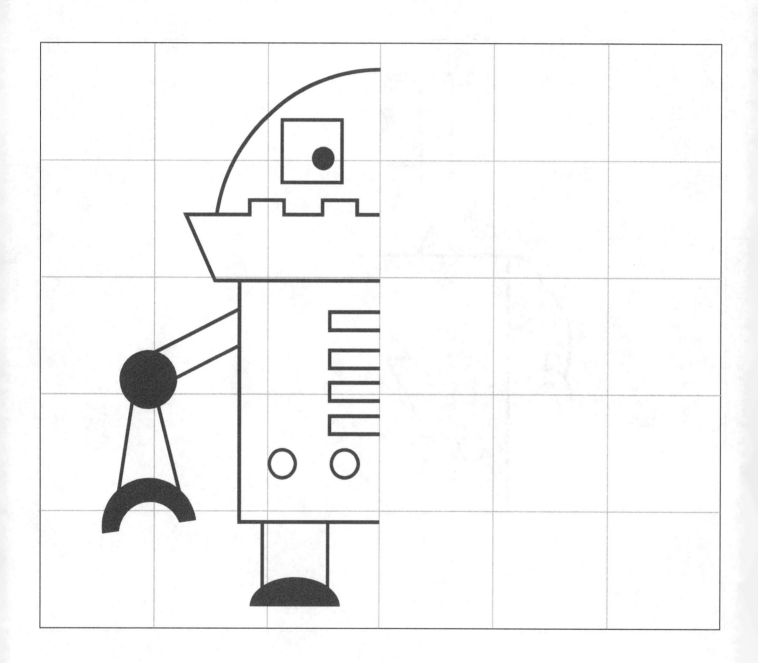

Get creative as you complete the image!

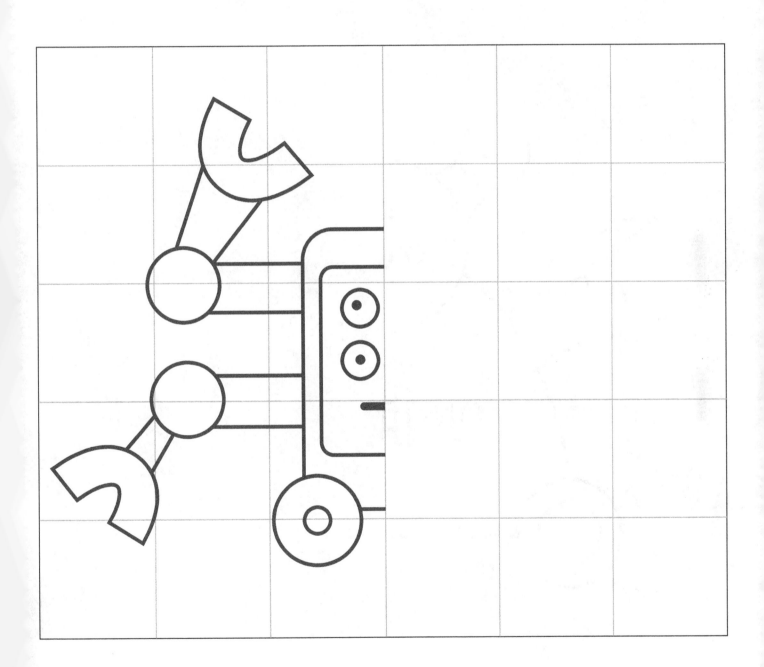

✏️ Get creative as you complete the image!

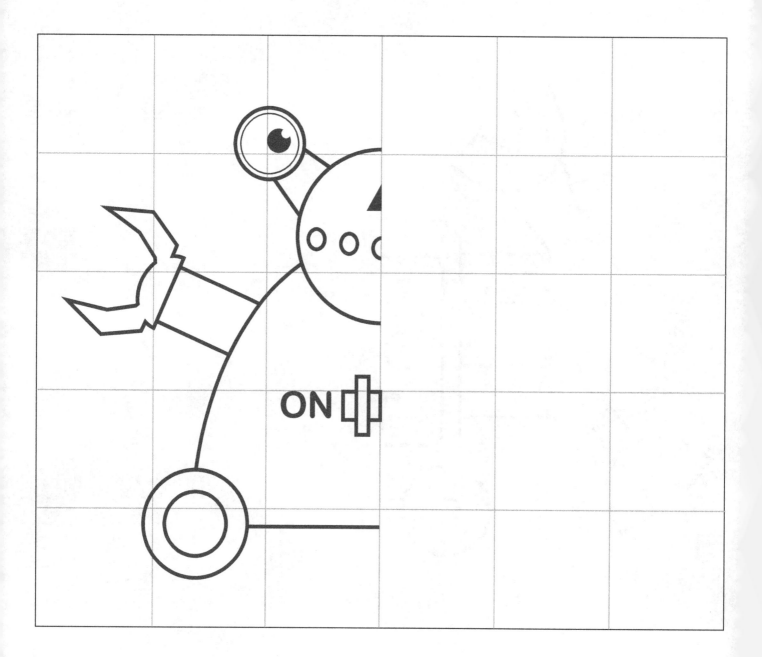

Get creative as you complete the image!

Get creative as you complete the image!

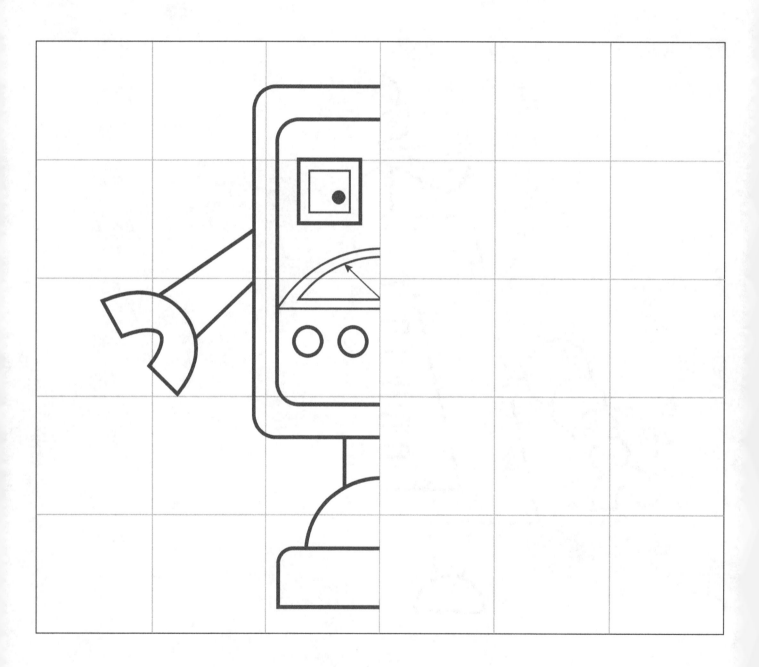

Get creative as you complete the image!

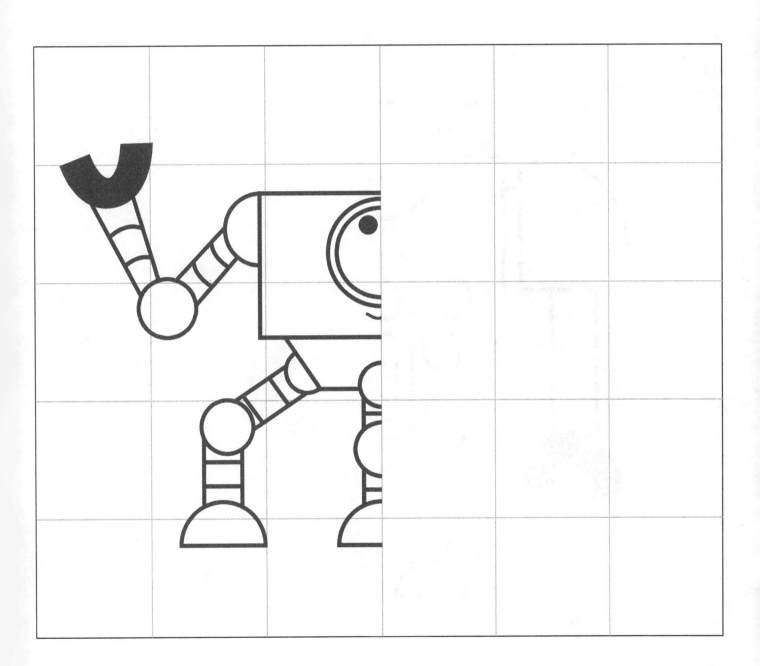

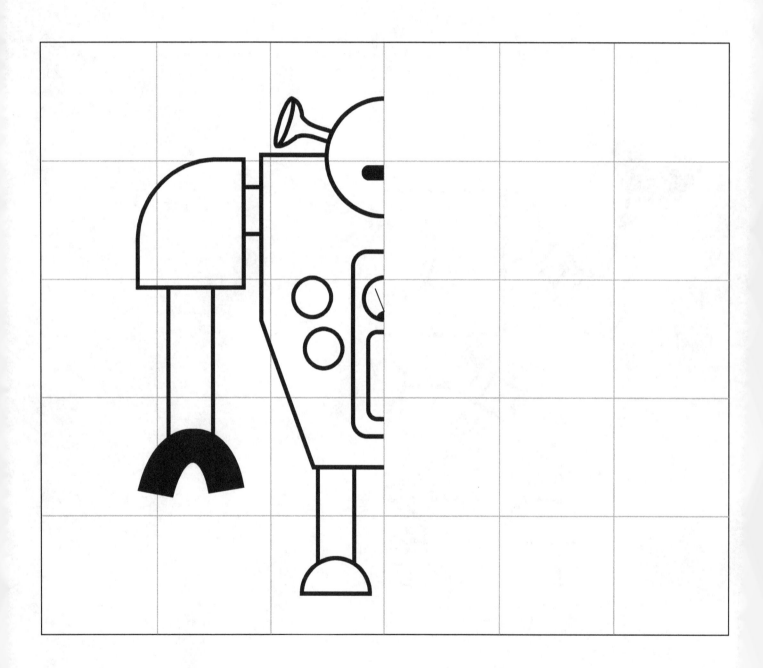

Get creative as you complete the image!

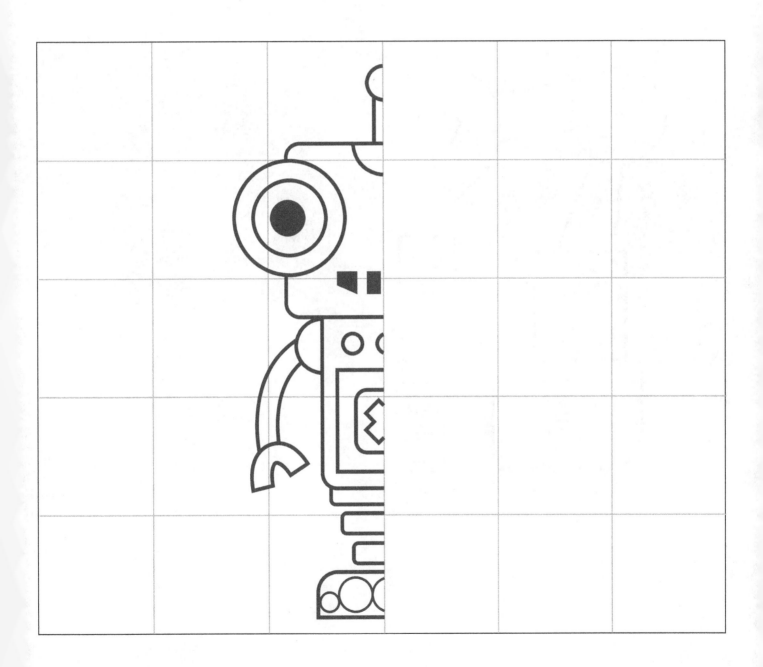

Get creative as you complete the image!

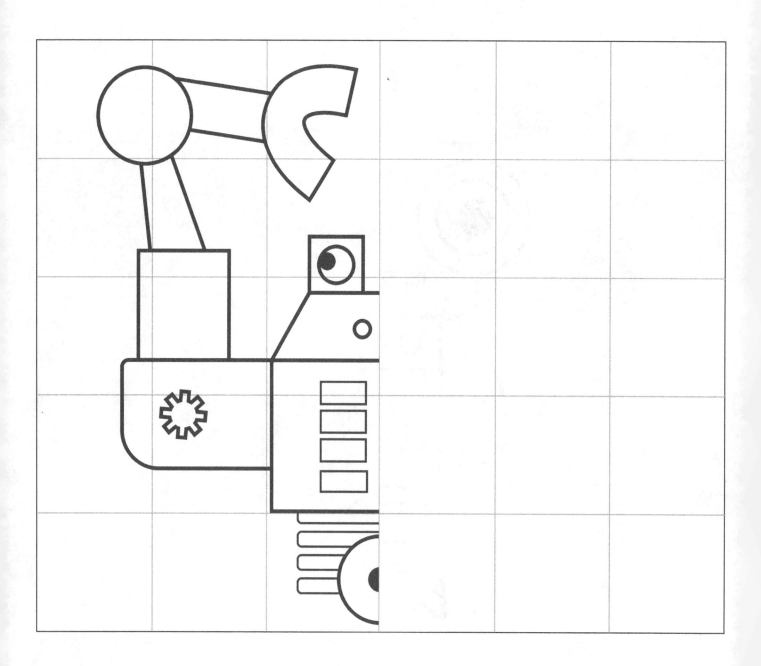

Get creative as you complete the image!

Get creative as you complete the image!

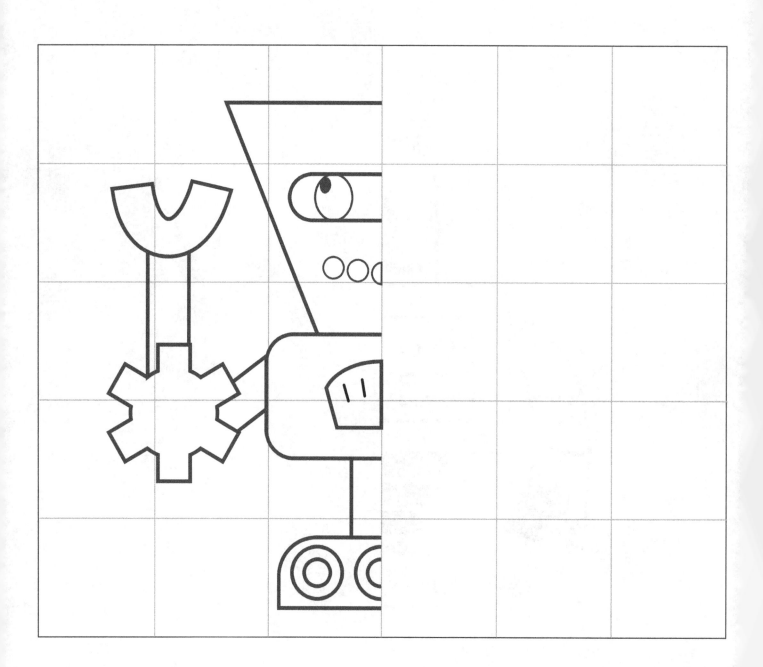

Get creative as you complete the image!

 Get creative as you complete the image!

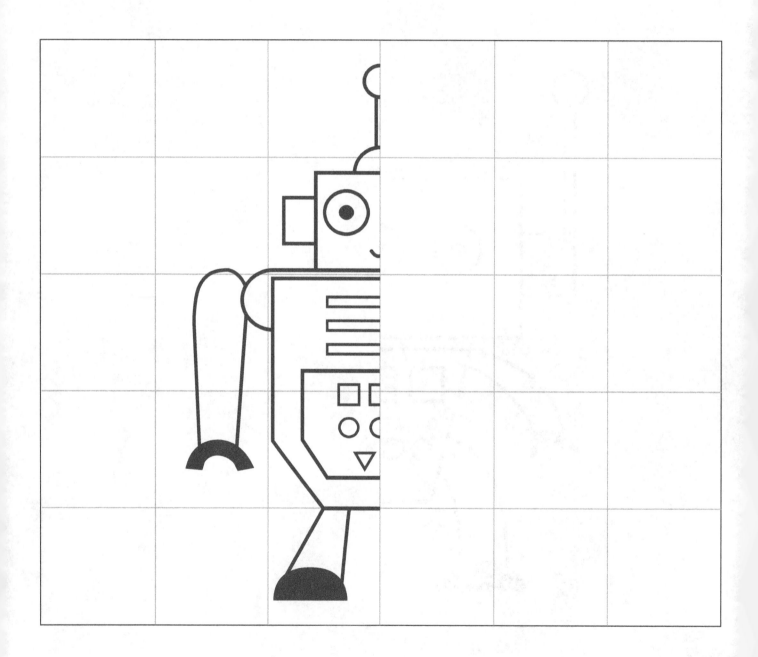

Get creative as you complete the image!

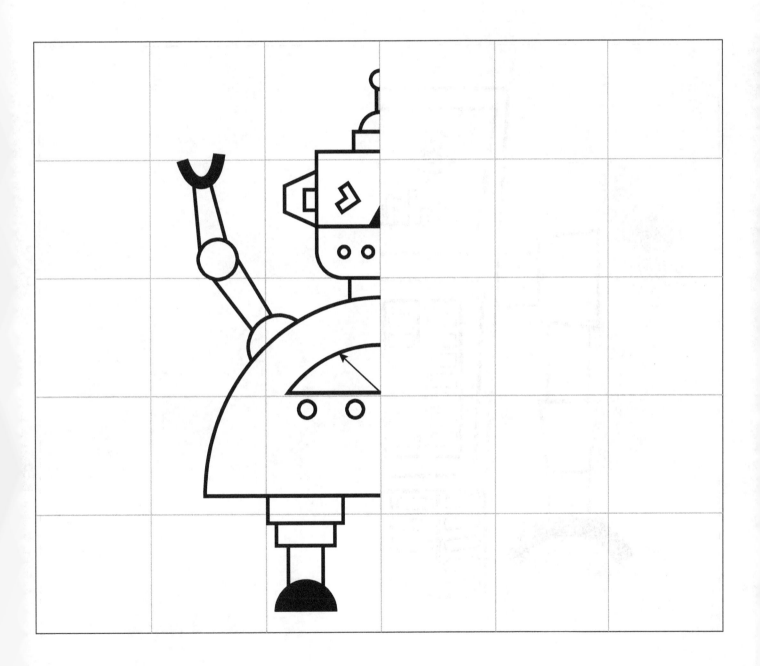

✏️ Get creative as you complete the image!

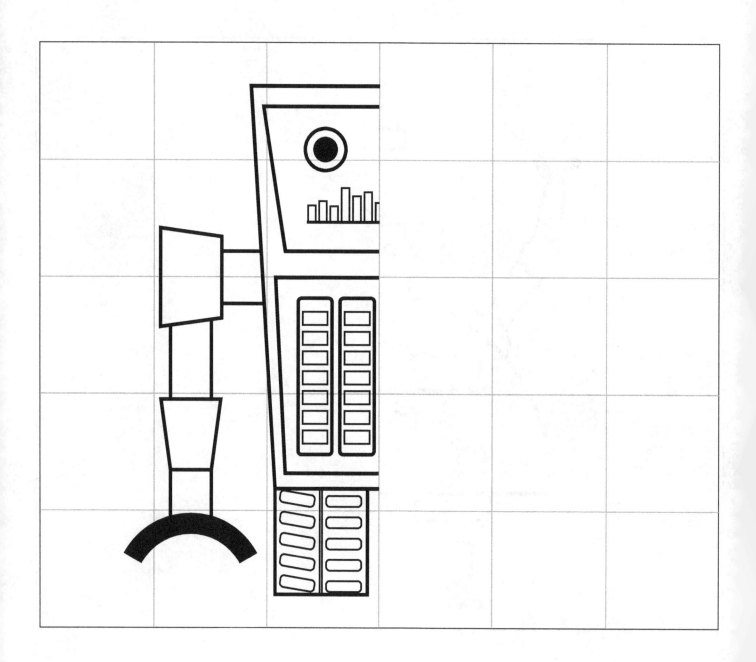

Get creative as you complete the image!

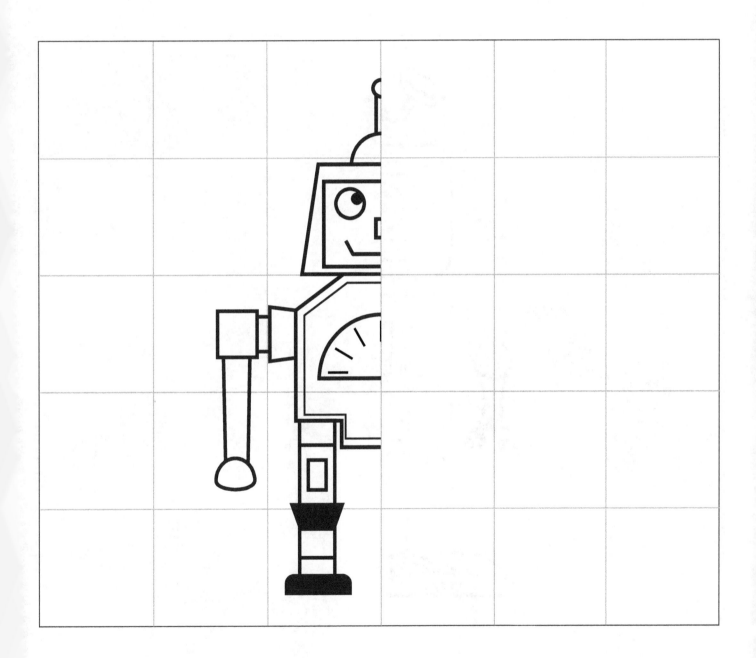

 Get creative as you complete the image!

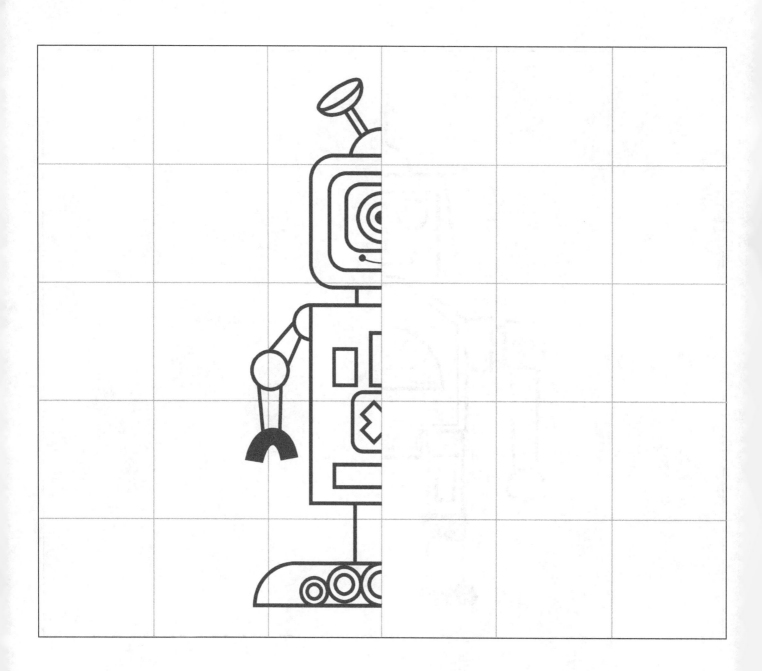

Get creative as you complete the image!

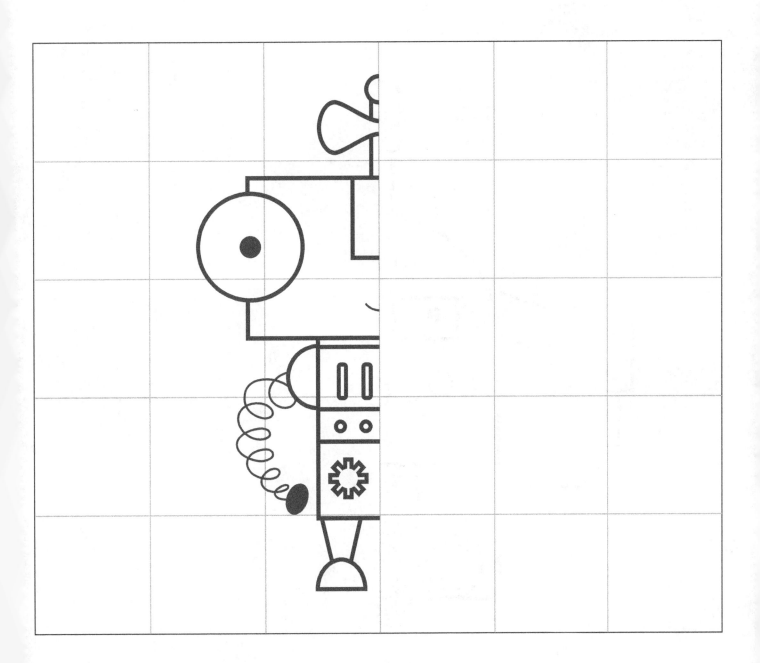

Get creative as you complete the image!

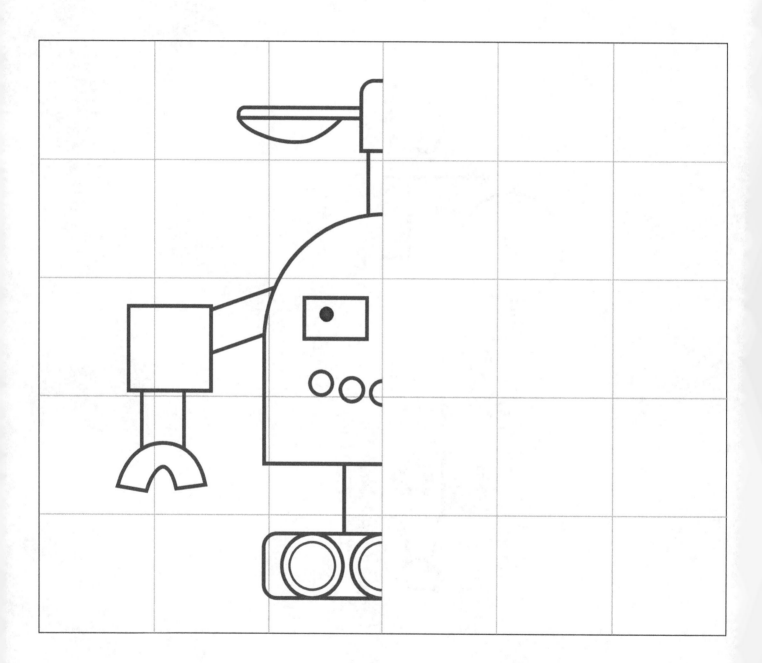

Get creative as you complete the image!

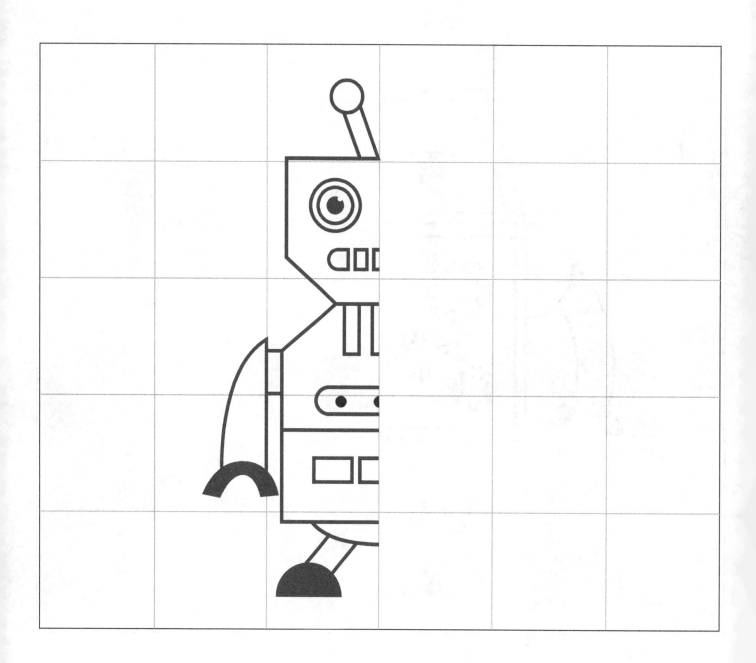

Get creative as you complete the image!

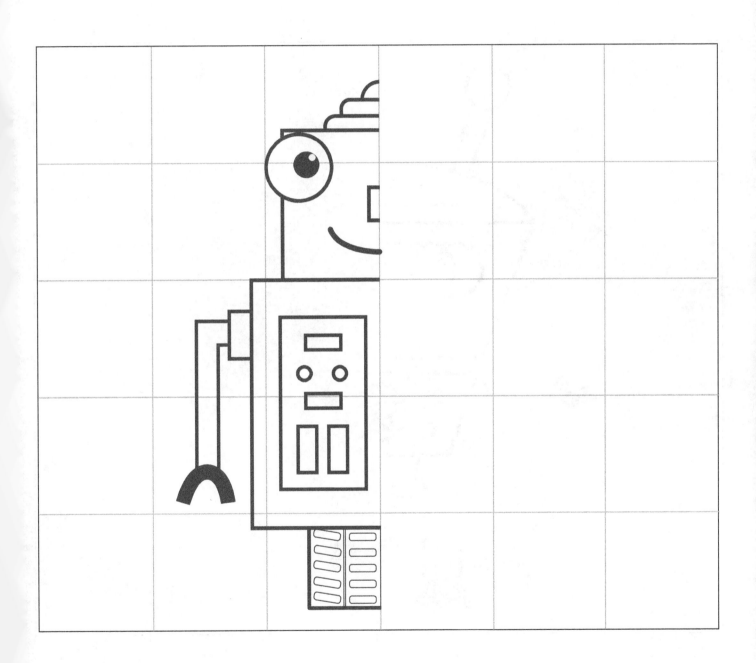

Get creative as you complete the image!

Get creative as you complete the image!

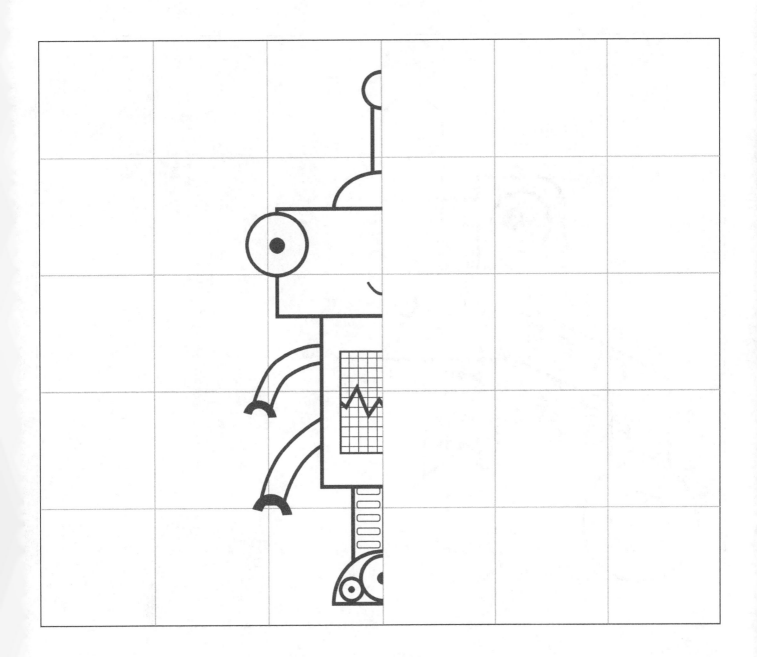

 Get creative as you complete the image!

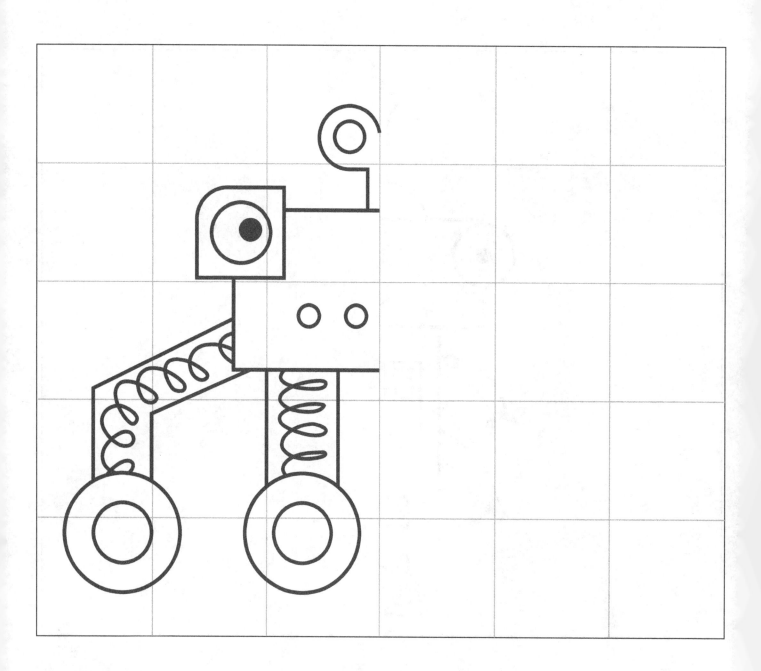

Get creative as you complete the image!

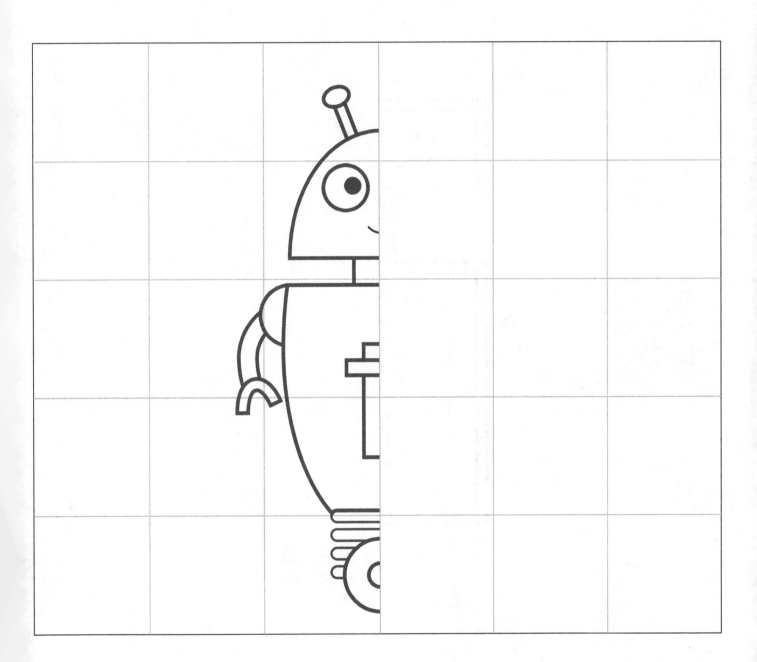

✏️ Get creative as you complete the image!

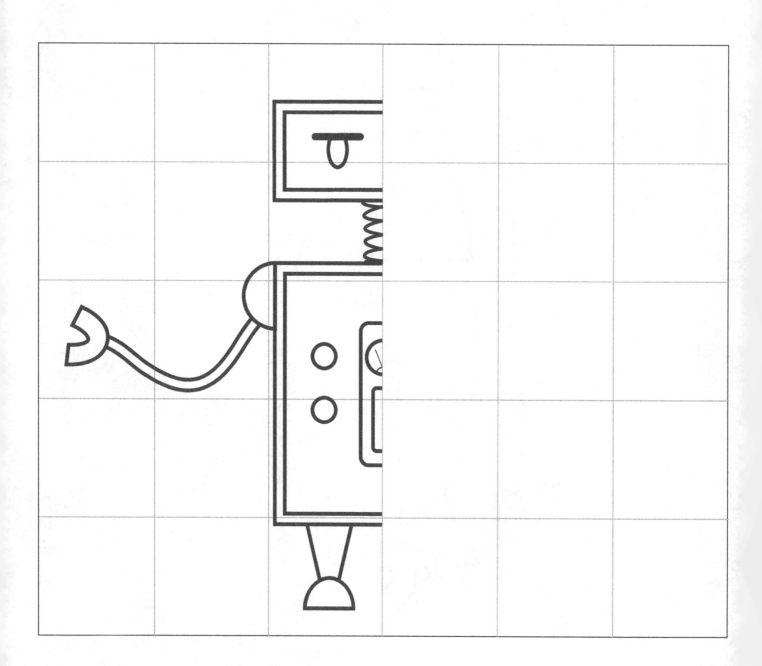

Get creative as you complete the image!

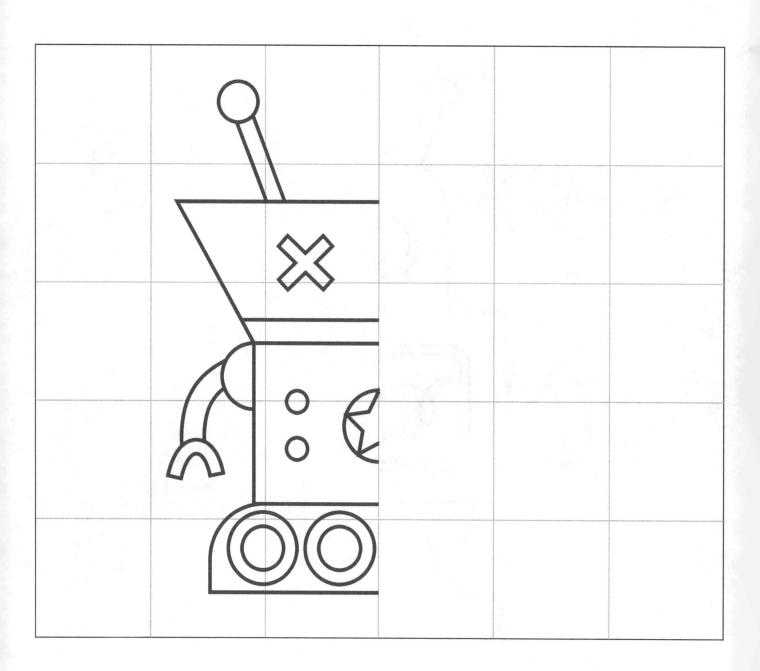

Get creative as you complete the image!

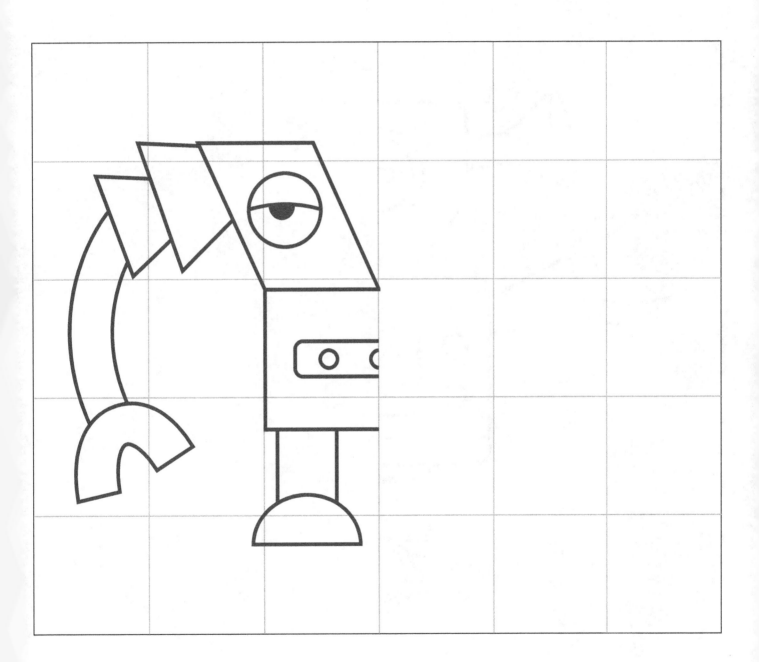

 Get creative as you complete the image!

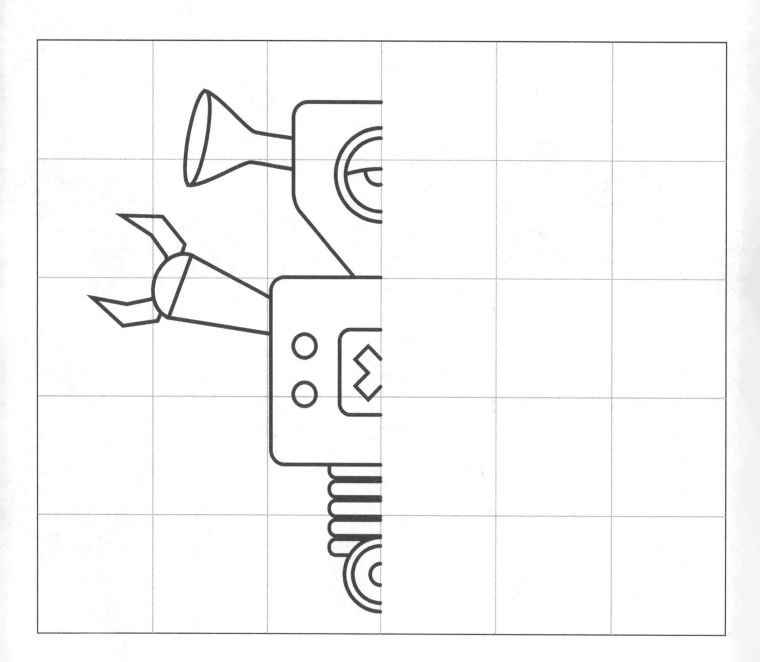

Get creative as you complete the image!

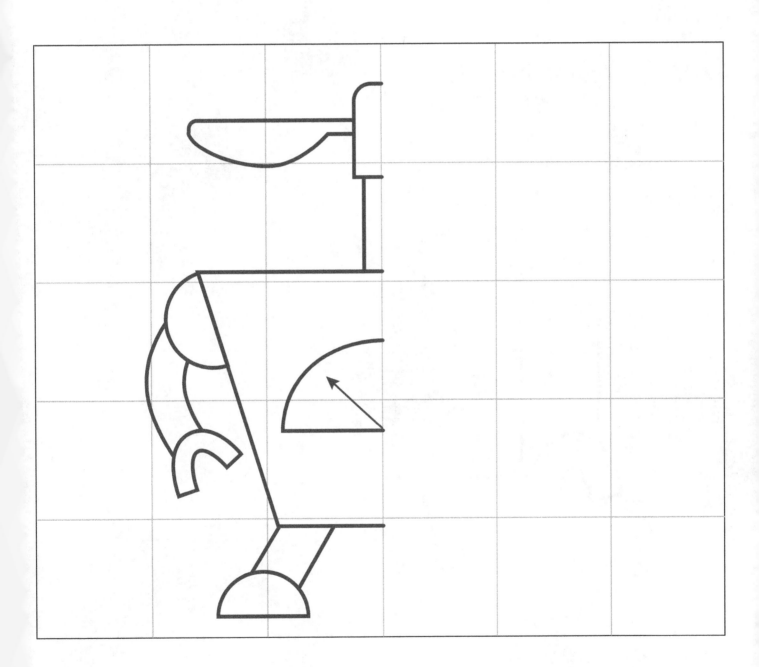

 Get creative as you complete the image!

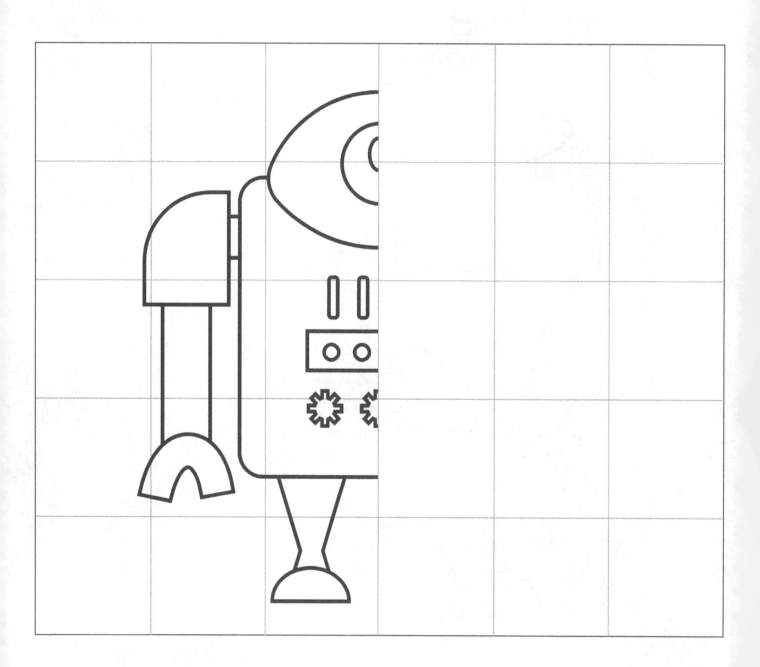

Get creative as you complete the image!

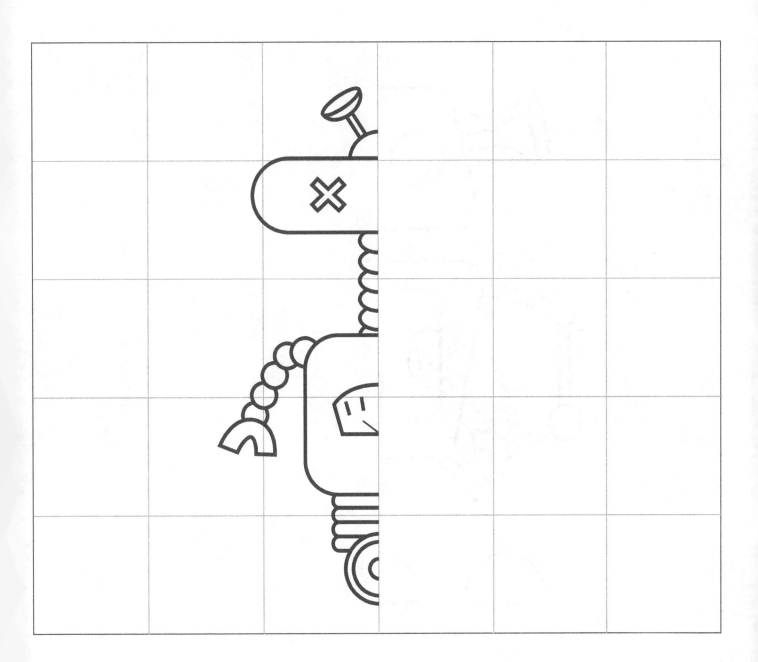

Get creative as you complete the image!

Get creative as you complete the image!

Get creative as you complete the image!

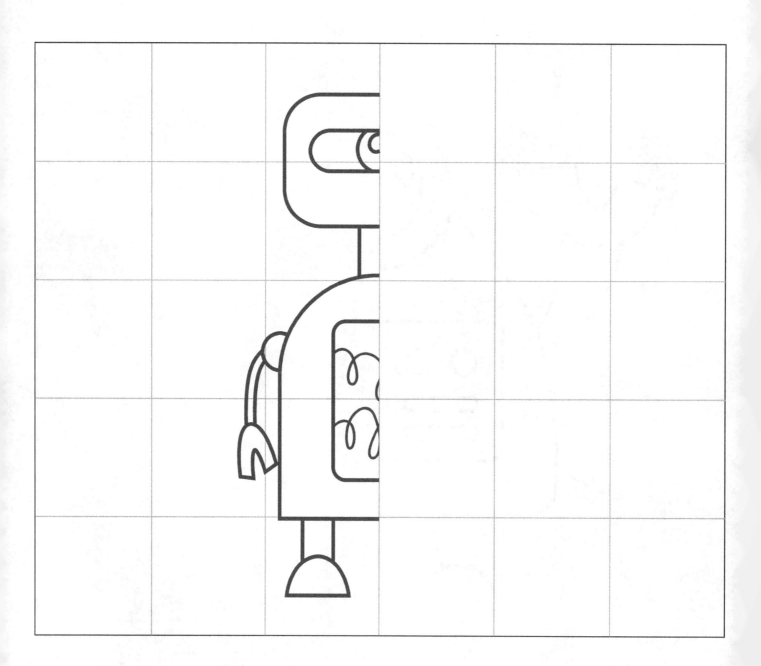

Get creative as you complete the image!

✏️ Get creative as you complete the image!

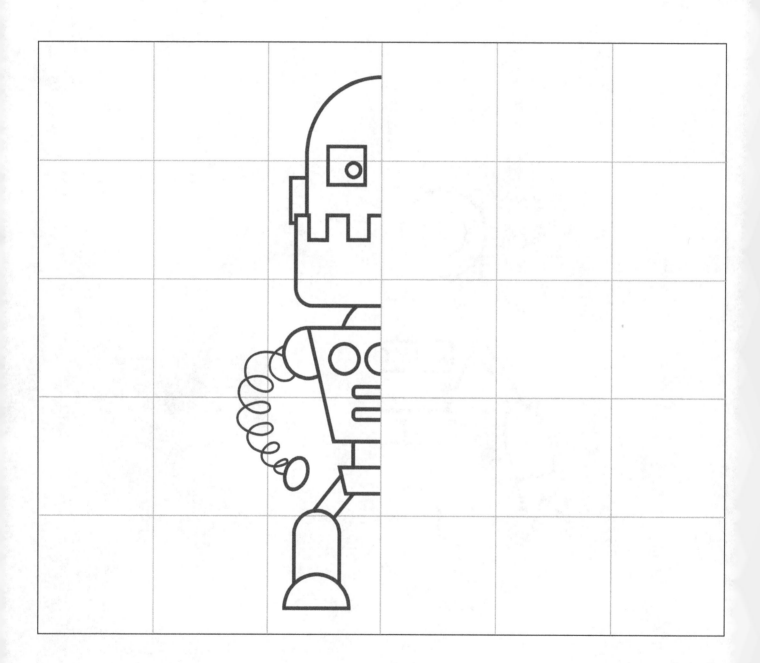

Get creative as you complete the image!

Get creative as you complete the image!

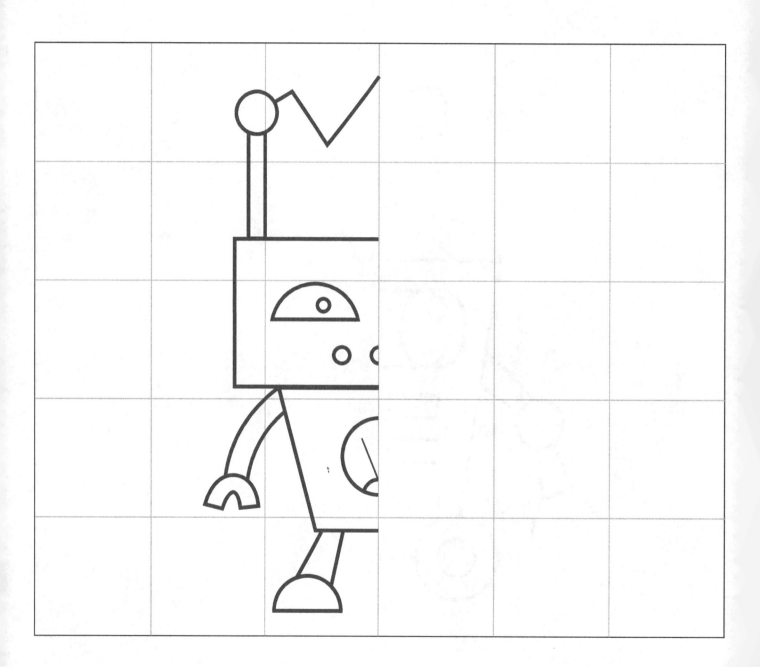

Get creative as you complete the image!

✏️ Get creative as you complete the image!

Get creative as you complete the image!

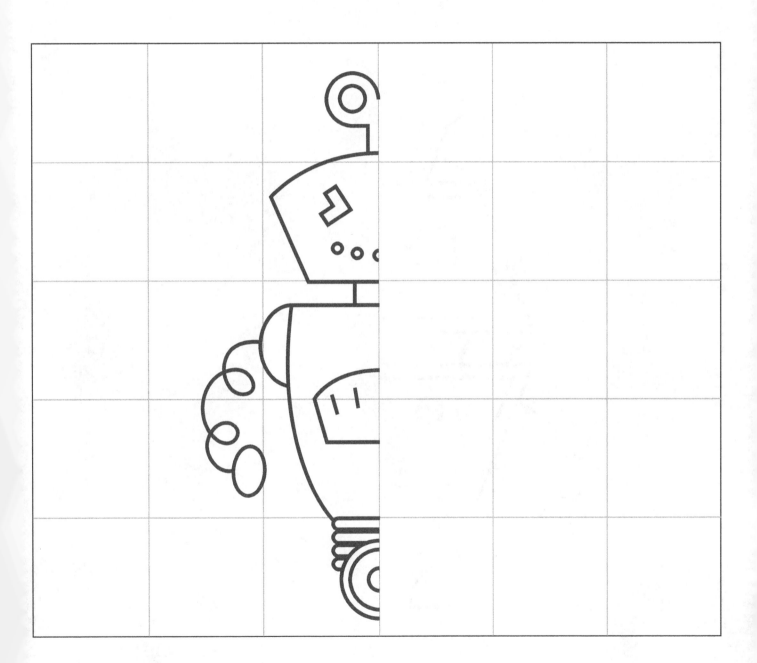

Get creative as you complete the image!

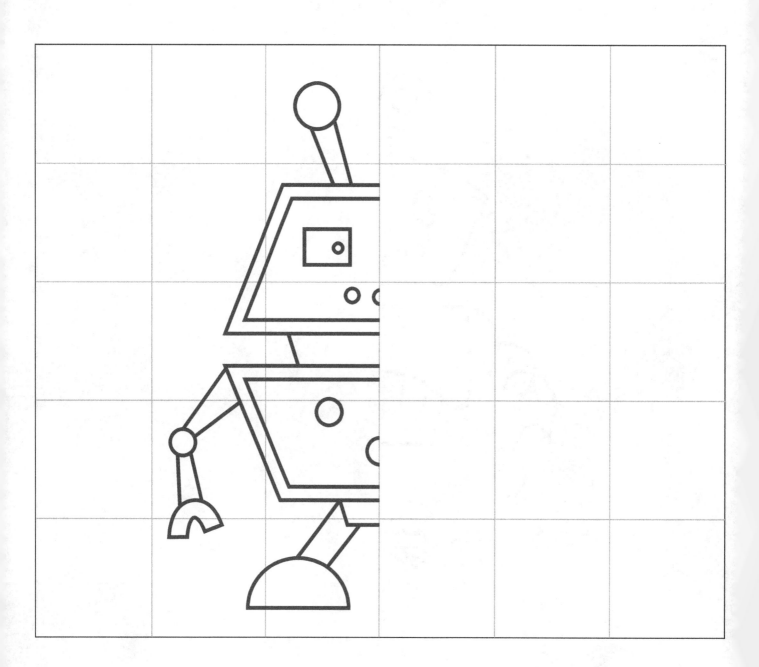

Get creative as you complete the image!

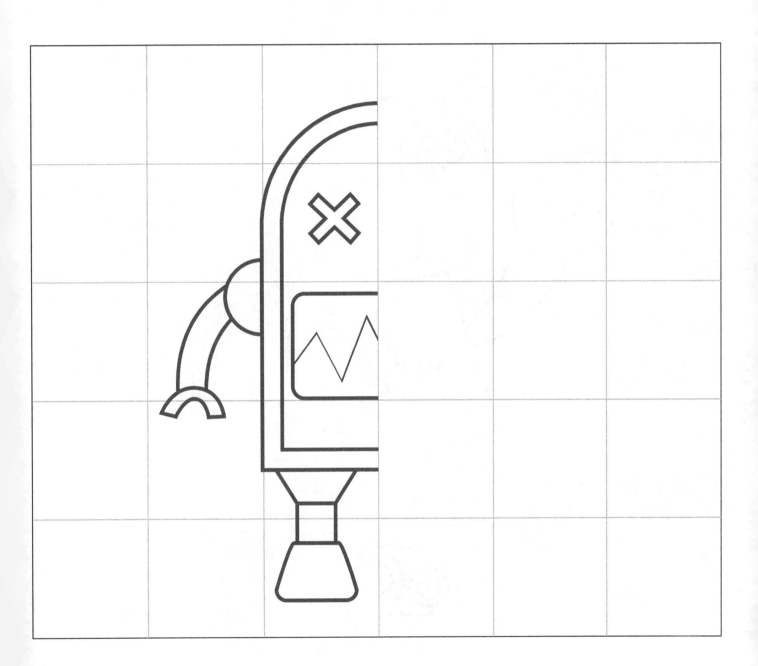

✏️ Get creative as you complete the image!

Get creative as you complete the image!

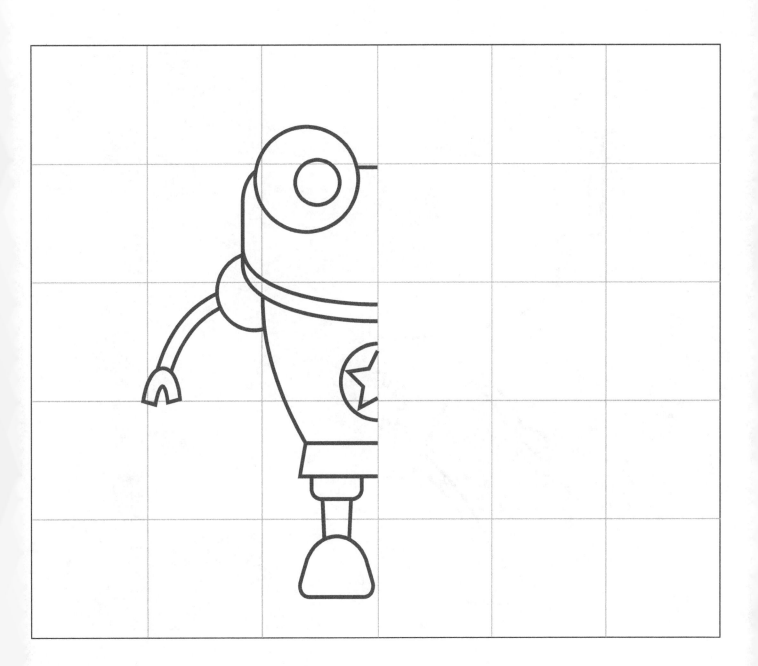

 Get creative as you complete the image!

Get creative as you complete the image!

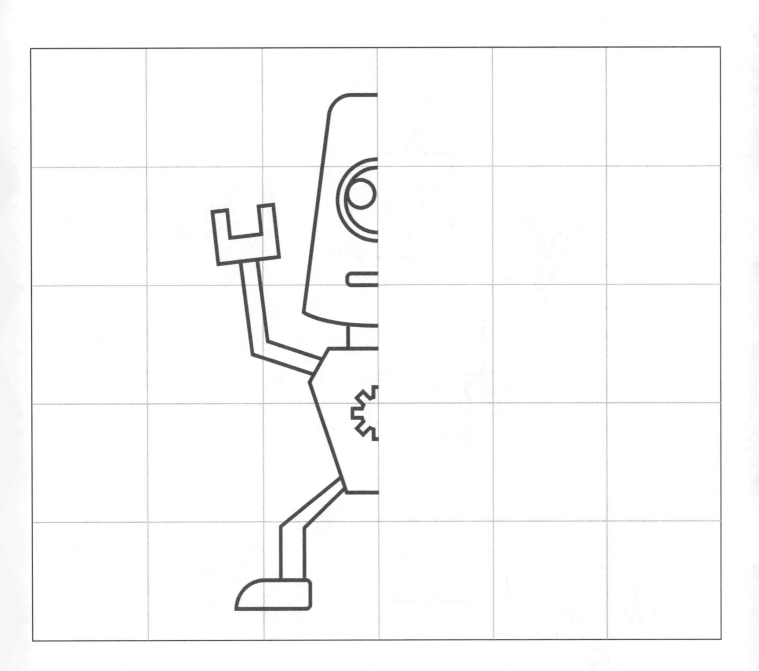

✏️ Get creative as you complete the image!

Get creative as you complete the image!

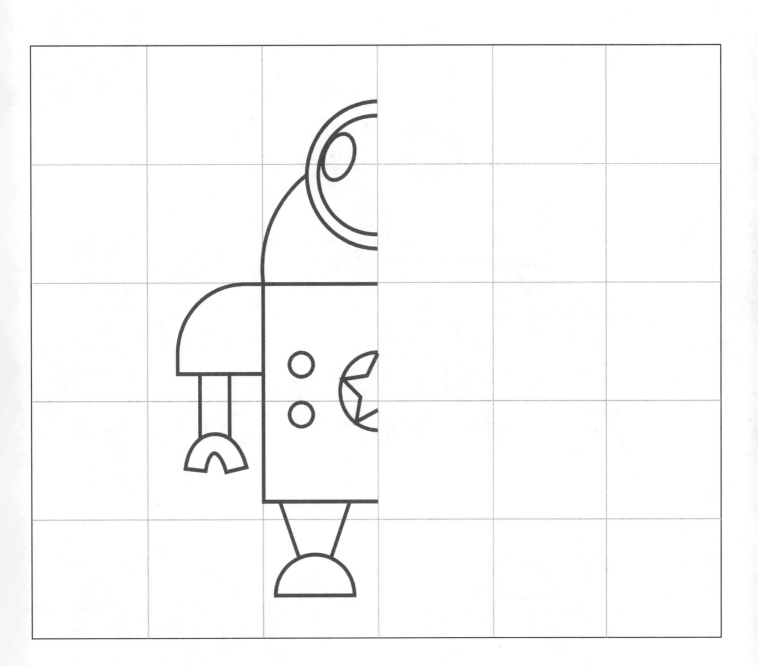

✏️ Get creative as you complete the image!

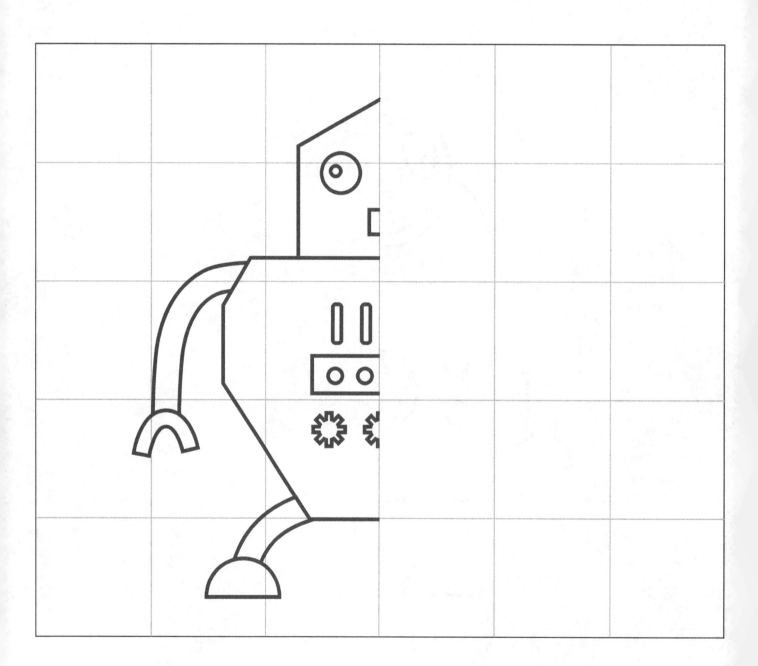

Get creative as you complete the image!

 Get creative as you complete the image!

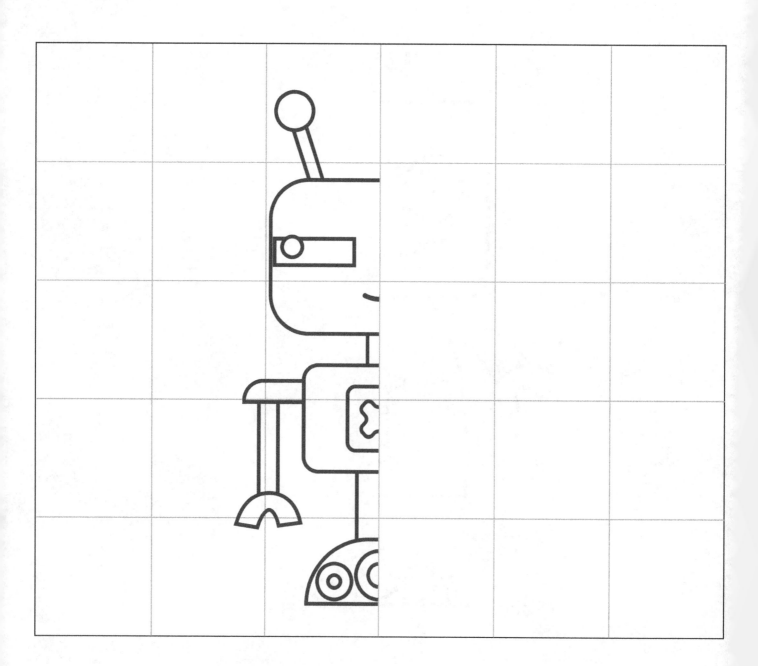

Get creative as you complete the image!

 Get creative as you complete the image!

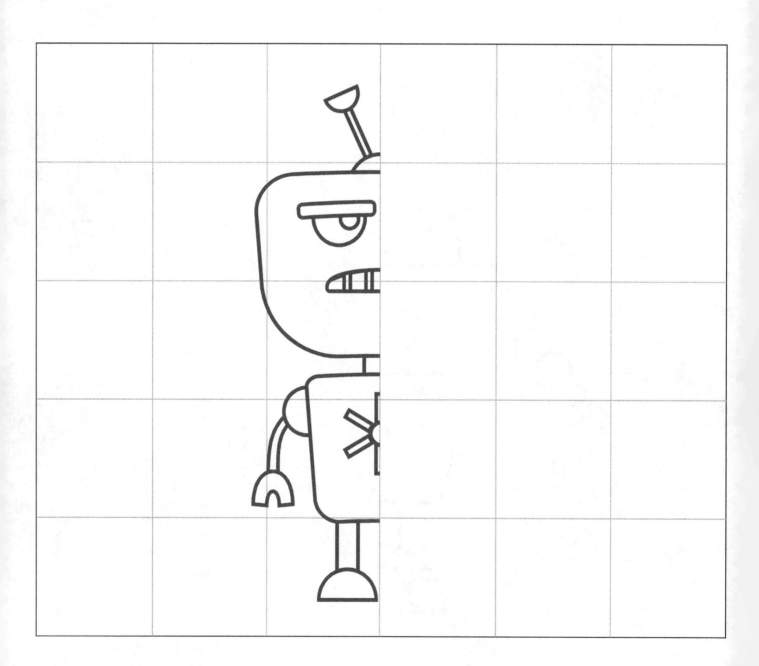

Get creative as you complete the image!

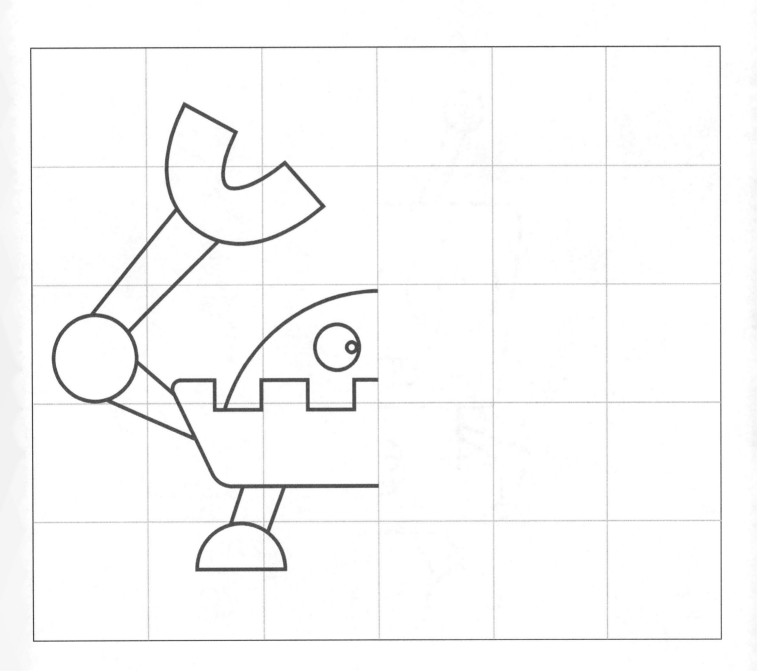

 Get creative as you complete the image!

Get creative as you complete the image!

Explore Activity Books at www.engagebooks.com

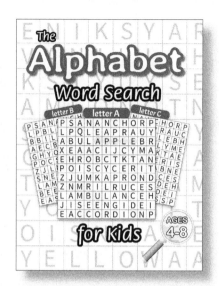

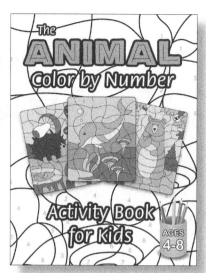

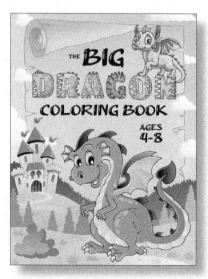

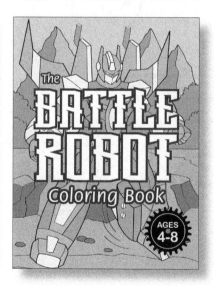

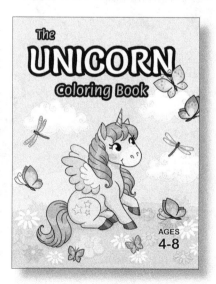

Explore Other Books at www.engagebooks.com

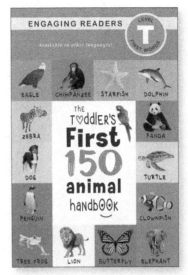

Have comments or suggestions?
Contact us at: alexis@engagebooks.ca

 Show us how you enjoy your **#engagingreaders**. Tweet a picture to **@engagebooks** for a chance to win free prizes.

CPSIA information can be obtained
at www.ICGtesting.com
Printed in the USA
LVHW061149301022
731921LV00030B/901

9 781774 7627